Graphic Organizers
for Language Arts Classes

by Daniel J. Barnekow

illustrated by Marcellus Hall

J. WESTON

WALCH

PUBLISHER

Portland, Maine

User's Guide
to
Walch Reproducible Books

As part of our general effort to provide educational materials that are as practical and economical as possible, we have designated this publication a "reproducible book." The designation means that purchase of the book includes purchase of the right to limited reproduction of all pages on which this symbol appears:

Here is the basic Walch policy: We grant to individual purchasers of this book the right to make sufficient copies of reproducible pages for use by all students of a single teacher. This permission is limited to a single teacher, and does not apply to entire schools or school systems, so institutions purchasing the book should pass the permission on to a single teacher. Copying of the book or its parts for resale is prohibited.

Any questions regarding this policy or requests to purchase further reproduction rights should be addressed to:

Permissions Editor
J. Weston Walch, Publisher
321 Valley Street • P.O. Box 658
Portland, Maine 04104-0658

1   2   3   4   5   6   7   8   9   10

ISBN 0-8251-3735-7

Contents

Preface

This book was conceived of as a kind of "Swiss Army knife" for English and language arts teachers. The idea was to create a teaching resource that would be there when you needed it, help you accomplish a wide variety of tasks, and get you out of some tough teaching spots.

That was the idea. The result is this book. Between its covers, you'll find a quick, prepared, practical assignment for virtually every major topic you're likely to cover in your language arts classes. What's more, each assignment is designed to teach, reinforce, and extend the key concepts of the language arts curriculum. This was accomplished by combining a teaching technique that has proven pedagogical value with national language arts curriculum standards.

You can draw on the student activity sheets in *Graphic Organizers for Language Arts Classes* nearly any school day. At your fingertips you'll have a ready-made, easy-to-use, pedagogically valuable lesson on nearly any topic. The lessons will be popular with students, and are suitable for either in-class or homework assignments.

We wish you, and your students, the best of luck in your endeavors.

My appreciation is extended to Lisa French, for her support while I assembled this book. More thanks go to the language arts teachers and, especially, their students, without whose insights this book would not be possible.

—*Daniel J. Barnekow*

To the Teacher

A teacher once described graphic organizers as "sophisticated doodles." In a way, he was right. In fact, that may be the best way for you to think about graphic organizers and to present them to your students. You can find many jargon-laden articles and books that analyze graphic organizers, put forth new taxonomies, and labor to link them to psychological dynamics. These have their place, of course, but graphic organizers—essentially a simple teaching tool—have been over-analyzed, with the net effect of confusing rather than enlightening educators.

Graphic Organizers for Language Arts Classes is designed to cut through the jargon and give you a practical tool that you can use immediately. By spending a little time reading this introduction and thumbing through the graphic organizers, you'll soon be ready to go.

Understanding Graphic Organizers

On a practical, classroom level, all you need to know about graphic organizers can be summed up in a few key points. As you use this book—or use graphic organizers in any educational context—keep these ideas in mind:

Graphic organizers are simply ways to organize information visually. This is a simple, straightforward, and accurate description of graphic organizers.

Graphic organizers are nearly always appropriate. Most people tend to think in visual terms, so graphic organizers are an appropriate way to organize information on a page.

Graphic organizers come in many forms. Many attempts have been made to categorize graphic organizers and to identify them by type. You've probably heard of sequence chains, concept maps, webs, flow charts, Venn diagrams, and so on. (You'll find all of these in this book.) Some of the best graphic organizers are combinations of these standard forms, and some are utterly unique.

Graphic organizers are never right or wrong, only better or worse. Assuming that the information presented and its interrelationships are correct, there are no "wrong" graphic organizers. However, some do a better job of presenting the same information than others.

Graphic organizers are not communicative, but conceptual. They are tools that help students acquire knowledge, and not a means of imparting knowledge. Obviously, graphic organizers are excellent communication tools, but in the classroom you should focus on using them as a way for students to learn, not as a way for them to express what they've learned to you.

Graphic organizers are concept-driven. The form of the graphic organizer should follow its function, not vice versa.

Content and Organization: Major Fields, Key Concepts, and Main Ideas

This book covers a wide range of language arts topics, as a glance at the table of contents will show. The major sections of the book correspond to *major fields* taught in language arts classes. Within each major field, the graphic organizers emphasize *key concepts,* and each graphic organizer focuses on the *main ideas* of a key concept.

This organization enables you to use these graphic organizers throughout the year to help students achieve the principal learning objectives of your language arts classes.

How to Use the Graphic Organizers in This Book

Of course, you can use these graphic organizers any way you see fit—they are flexible tools. You can use them for basal instruction, review, and extension and enrichment. You can have students work in pairs or small groups to complete them. They function equally well for homework and in-class assignments and are also excellent guides for classroom discussion.

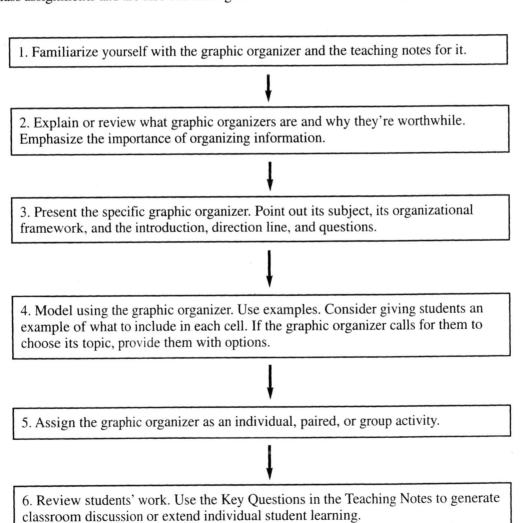

1. Familiarize yourself with the graphic organizer and the teaching notes for it.

2. Explain or review what graphic organizers are and why they're worthwhile. Emphasize the importance of organizing information.

3. Present the specific graphic organizer. Point out its subject, its organizational framework, and the introduction, direction line, and questions.

4. Model using the graphic organizer. Use examples. Consider giving students an example of what to include in each cell. If the graphic organizer calls for them to choose its topic, provide them with options.

5. Assign the graphic organizer as an individual, paired, or group activity.

6. Review students' work. Use the Key Questions in the Teaching Notes to generate classroom discussion or extend individual student learning.

A Lesson Cycle for Individual Graphic Organizers. Educators have learned that following a few simple steps will help their students get the most out of their graphic organizers. These steps, tailored to the content of this book, are presented below in, well, a graphic organizer!

How to Use the Graphic Organizers As a Set

Because *Graphic Organizers for Language Arts Classes* has nearly comprehensive topic coverage based on national standards, you can use the organizers as curricular signposts, correlating them to the main points in your curriculum.

Also, because the graphic organizers emphasize main ideas in the key concepts of major areas of language arts education study, they are excellent material for student portfolios.

Teaching Notes

Teaching notes for each of the graphic organizers in this book are provided at the beginning of each major section in the text. The notes are organized as follows:

[number]
[Title of Graphic Organizer]

Objective
    Identifies the major learning objective of the graphic organizer

Key Questions
    Key questions that generate classroom discussion, guide students in achieving the learning objective, and extend teaching about the subject of the graphic organizer

Usage Notes
    Tips and techniques for using the graphic organizer most effectively; included when useful

---

I.   Vocabulary

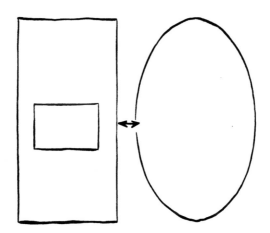

1. Vocabulary

This set of graphic organizers gives an overview of the concept of vocabulary and its importance, and sets students to work on enhancing their own vocabulary.

V-1: What Is Vocabulary?

Objective: Students will define *vocabulary* and explain its importance.

Key Questions:

- What is vocabulary?
- Why is it important?
- What can you do to improve your vocabulary?

Usage Notes: This graphic organizer works well as a whole-class activity.

V-2: Vertical Vocabulary

Objective: Students will explore important aspects of vocabulary.

Key Questions:

- Questions formed from each sentence in the graphic organizer

Usage Notes: This graphic organizer works well as a homework activity. Consider modeling one or more of the sentence completions for students.

V-3: Making Words My Own

Objective: Students will track their acquisition of new words.

Key Questions:

- Which words were easier for you to learn? Harder?
- Did you skip any steps when learning some of these words?
- How will understanding this process help you learn new words in the future?

Usage Notes: Coordinate using this graphic organizer with your regular vocabulary instruction. Distribute a new copy of this graphic organizer when you introduce a new set of vocabulary words.

V-4: Synonyms and Antonyms of a Word

Objective: Students will identify the synonyms and antonyms of a word.

Key Questions:

- What are synonyms? Antonyms?
- What are some synonyms for this word?

- What are some antonyms?
- How can you go about finding more synonyms and antonyms?
- Why is knowing synonyms and antonyms important?

Usage Notes: Distribute multiple copies of this graphic organizer.

V-5: Creating a Word Profile

Objective: Students will investigate important qualities of a word.

Key Questions:
- What does this word mean?
- Why is it important to know this word?
- What are some examples of how you might use this word?

Usage Notes: Distribute multiple copies of this graphic organizer.

V-6: Tracing a Word's Development

Objective: Students will explain the etymology of a word.

Key Questions:
- What is the origin of this word?
- How old is this word?
- What changes have occurred to this word over time?

Usage Notes: Distribute multiple copies of this graphic organizer.

V-7: A Personal Word Log

Objective: Students will keep a personal word log.

Key Questions:
- What words have you added to your log?
- Where did you first encounter them?
- What does each one mean?
- What is an interesting fact about each word (origin, pronunciation, etc.)?

Usage Notes: Encourage students to keep their logs and update them weekly.

Name _____ Date _____

V-1: What Is Vocabulary?

Introduction: What exactly does vocabulary mean? Why is it important? How can you improve your own vocabulary? This activity will help you answer these questions.

• **Directions:** Complete the graphic organizer by thinking about vocabulary and writing information in each box.

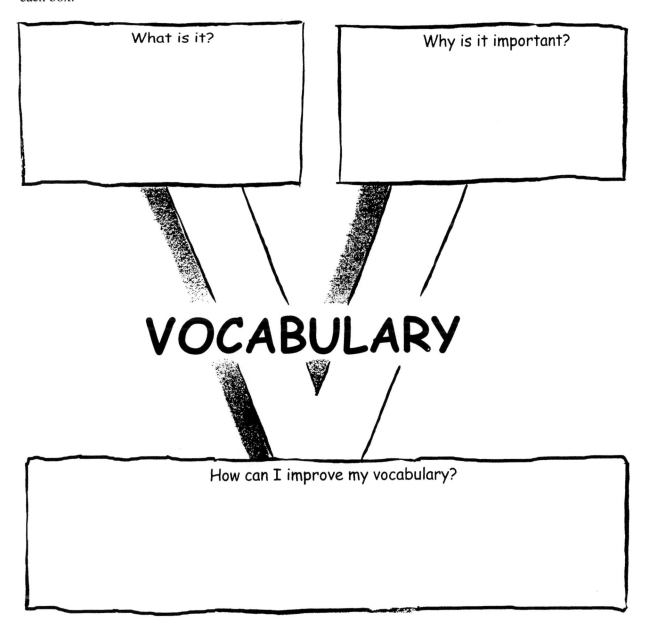

What is it?

Why is it important?

VOCABULARY

How can I improve my vocabulary?

Taking Another Step: Use a dictionary to find out where the word **vocabulary** comes from.

Name _____ Date _____ | **Student Activity Sheet**

V-2: Vertical Vocabulary

Introduction: As people meet and get to know you, they form a picture of you in their mind and decide whether they like you. Your vocabulary is one of the most important things that people take into account when forming an opinion about you. This activity will help you think about your vocabulary, and how to improve it.

• **Directions:** Complete each sentence in the "Vertical Vocabulary" box.

V
E
R
T
I
C
A
L

V
O
C
A
B
U
L
A
R
Y

Vocabulary is _____
_____.

One reason vocabulary is important to me is _____
_____.

Clever ways for me to remember the meanings of words are _____
_____.

A new word I learned recently is _____
_____.

By improving my vocabulary, I also improve _____
_____.

Using new words when I speak and write is important because ____
_____.

Learning new words is important to me because _____
_____.

*A word I don't yet know but would like to learn the meaning of is ___
_____.

Reading helps me improve my vocabulary because _____
_____.

You to need to improve your vocabulary constantly because _____
_____.

Taking Another Step: Use a dictionary to find out the meaning of the word you wrote after the "A" with the star by it. Write the definition on the back of this sheet.

Name _____ Date _____

V-3: Making Words My Own

Introduction: Every time you learn a new word, you follow the same steps. At the beginning, you've never heard of the word. Then, you hear the word for the first time, but you're not sure what it means. Next, you begin to get some idea of what it means. When you've read and heard the word a number of times, you know what it means, but you really never use it. Finally, you make the word your own. You add it to your vocabulary by knowing it and using it. This activity will help you track this process.

• **Directions:** Write a new word on each line of the first column. In the middle columns, note the date when you reach each step for each word. Finally, when you make a word your own, write that date in the last column along with its definition and an example of when you used it.

	Making Words My Own!				
	How Well I Know the Word				
	Never heard of it!	Heard it but have no idea what it means	Have some idea of what it means	Know what it means but don't use it	It's my word! I know it, I use it, and here's what it means:
Word	start →	⟶	⟶	⟶	→finish!
1.					
2.					
3.					
4.					
5.					

Taking Another Step: Write a paragraph on the back of this sheet that explains why one of the words in the chart was or was not easy for you to learn.

Name _____ Date _____

V-4: Synonyms and Antonyms

Introduction: As you know, **synonyms** are words that have the same or similar meanings. For example, what synonyms can you think of for *hot.* (warm, boiling, fiery . . .) **Antonyms** are words that have opposite, or nearly opposite, meanings. What are some antonyms for *hot?* (cold, cool, icy . . .) Knowing the synonyms and antonyms for a word is important to understanding and using it properly. In this activity, you'll identify several synonyms and antonyms for a word.

• **Directions:** Write the word in the center box. Then list as many synonyms and antonyms of the word as you can in the correct places.

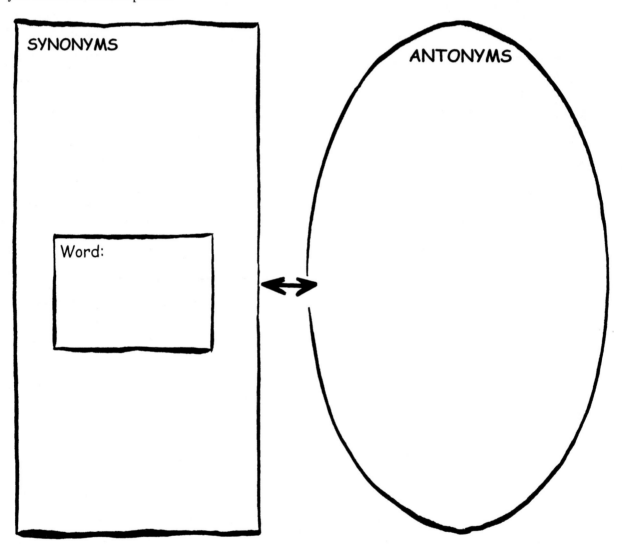

Taking Another Step: Circle the synonym with the meaning that is closest to the word's. Then, circle the antonym whose meaning is closest to being the exact opposite.

8   *Graphic Organizers for Language Arts Classes*

Name _____ Date _____

V-5: Creating a Word Profile

Introduction: Words don't exist by themselves. Every word has many things associated with it. For example, each word has a **definition**, **synonyms**, and **antonyms**. A word can be used in different **contexts**—different situations that give it different meanings. Knowing all of these things about a word lets you create a word profile that will help you learn, remember, and understand the word so it becomes part of your vocabulary.

• **Directions:** Complete the word profile below for a word of your choice.

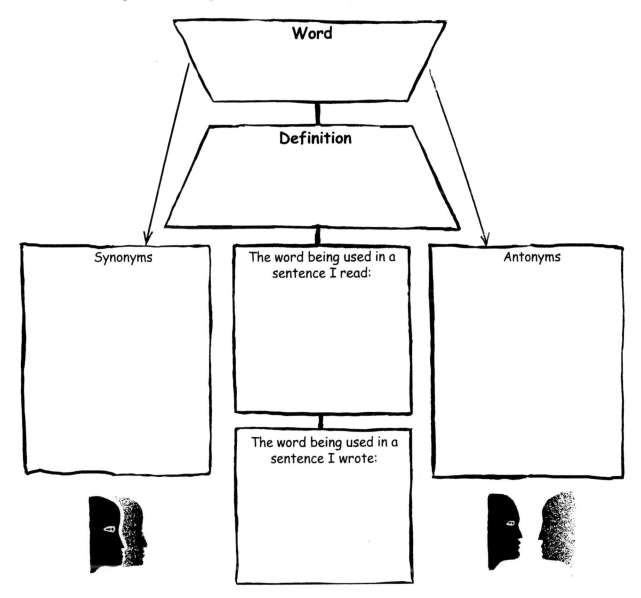

Taking Another Step: Add a box to the profile that explains the origin of the word. Or, add a box to the profile that shows the word's parts.

   Graphic Organizers for Language Arts Classes

Name _____ Date _____

V-6: Tracing a Word's Development

Introduction: Have you ever thought about why we use the words we do? Someone didn't look up one day and say, "Hey, let's call that thing over there a desk!" Words aren't made up—they develop over time. The history of how a word developed is called its **etymology**. An etymology is like a biography: It tells when a word was born and how it changed and grew over time. Knowing a word's etymology will help you understand the word's meaning, remember it, and use it in speaking and writing.

• **Directions:** Write a word in the top oval. Then, use a dictionary to find out the etymology of the word. Cross out any oval you don't need.

Our Word

which came from
Language:
Word:
Meaning:

which came from
Language:
Word:
Meaning:

which came from
Language:
Word:
Meaning:

which came from
Language:
Word:
Meaning:

Taking Another Step: Explain how knowing this word's etymology helps you understand it better.

    10   *Graphic Organizers for Language Arts Classes*

Name _____ Date _____

V-7: A Personal Word Log

Introduction: There are a mind-boggling 600,000 words in the English language! If you learned 24 new words a day—one every hour around the clock—it would still take you almost 70 years to learn them all. Of course, no one knows them all, but the more words you know, the better off you'll be. One good way to learn new words is to jot them down in a personal word log. Try to include something you find interesting about each word.

• **Directions:** As you encounter new and interesting words, add them to your word log. Be sure to note something interesting about each word—its meaning, origin, how it's used, where you read it, and so on.

Word Log	
Word	Important facts

Taking Another Step: Write sentences using your new words on the back of this sheet.

II. Literature: Setting, Plot, and Character

This set of graphic organizers introduces students to basic ideas about setting, plot, and character in literature, and helps them see connections between these concepts in literature and in life.

L-1: What Is Literature?

Objective: Students will explain the meaning of the term *literature* and discuss its important characteristics.

Key Questions:
- What is literature?
- What qualities does literature have that set it apart from other writing?
- Why do people write and read literature?
- What literature have you read recently?

Usage Notes: Encourage students to appreciate the universality of literature.

L-2: An Author Profile

Objective: Students will create a biographical profile of an author.

Key Questions:
- Why do you like this author?
- What are his or her major works?
- If you could meet this author, what would you like to say to him or her?

Usage Notes: This graphic organizer can also be used with authors of nonfiction works. Encourage students to try to contact living authors they selected.

L-3: A Book Summary

Objective: Students will summarize a book chapter-by-chapter.

Key Questions:
- Which chapter was most interesting to you? Why?
- How does summarizing the book help you?
- Why is it important to include just the key, or major, events and ideas in a summary?

Usage Notes: This graphic organizer can also be used with nonfiction works. Encourage students to summarize each chapter immediately after they finish reading it.

LP-1: What Is Plot?

Objective: Students will define *plot* and investigate some of its most important aspects.

Key Questions:

- Questions from the graphic organizer.

Usage Notes: Emphasize the fundamental importance of plot to literature.

LP-2: Mapping a Plot

Objective: Students will map the exposition, rising action, climax, falling action, and resolution of the plot of a story.

Key Questions:

- How was the exposition accomplished?
- What events made up the rising action? The falling action?
- What was the climax of the story?
- What conflict or conflicts occur in the story?
- How are they resolved?

Usage Notes: Use this graphic organizer to link fundamental concepts of plot with other important concepts in literature, especially characterization and suspense.

LP-3: Plot and Subplots

Objective: Students will identify and summarize the subplots of a story.

Key Questions:

- What is a subplot?
- Why did the author include subplots?
- What was the rising action, climax, falling action, and resolution of each subplot?
- Did the subplots enhance or detract from the main story?

Usage Notes: Use examples of plots with and without their subplots to help students appreciate how subplots fill out a literary work.

LP-4: Answering Questions About an Event in a Plot

Objective: Students will identify a key event in a plot and answer fundamental questions about it.

Key Questions:

- Questions from the graphic organizer

Usage Notes: Distribute multiple copies of this graphic organizer. Consider using the climax as the event to focus on in this activity.

LP-5: A Circle Map of a Story

Objective: Students will identify the key events in a plot and discuss the concept of "completeness" in a story.

Key Questions:

- How does the author take you "full circle" in this story?

- How is this related to the sense of "completeness" the reader feels?

- Why do so many stories follow this pattern?

Usage Notes: Work to make sure students understand the concept of "completeness" or "wholeness" in this context.

LP-6: A Storyboard

Objective: Students will create a storyboard to summarize a story.

Key Questions:

- What is a storyboard?

- Why is it a good way to summarize a story?

- How could a storyboard be used if someone made a movie based on a book?

Usage Notes: This graphic organizer works well with lower-level students and with visual learners.

LP-7: Events/Decision Chain

Objective: Students will explore how characters' decisions have consequences that lead to plot development.

Key Questions:

- How did decisions made by characters lead to each event in the plot?

- Why did the characters make the decisions they did?

- How would the results change if characters made different decisions?

Usage Notes: Explain and emphasize the concept of action and consequence, or cause and effect, underscoring that multiple causes and effects combine to make events.

LC-1: Character Traits

Objective: Students will identify a character's main social, emotional, mental, and physical traits.

Key Questions:

- What are this character's most important mental traits? Physical traits? Emotional traits? Social traits?

- Which traits seem to dominate the others?

- How do these traits explain the character's role in the story?

- What are some consequences of each trait?

Usage Notes: Emphasize that the character is made up of all of these traits.

LC-2: Clues About a Character

Objective: Students will identify and explain the clues they used to make inferences about a character.

Key Questions:

- What clues led you to believe the character has each trait?

- Were some traits easier to identify than others? Why?

Usage Notes: Distribute multiple copies of this graphic organizer so students can analyze and compare and contrast all of the main characters in a reading assignment. Respect students' privacy in the Taking Another Step activity.

LC-3: A Character Circle Graph

Objective: Students will create a circle graph to identify the relative importance of a character's traits.

Key Questions:

- Which trait or traits seem to dominate this character?

- Why do you think so?

- Which trait has the most effect on the other characters in the story? On the plot?

Usage Notes: Respect students' privacy in the Taking Another Step activity. Emphasize the multidimensionality of well-drawn literary characters.

LC-4: A Character's Problem and Solution

Objective: Students will investigate and map a problem that a character is facing and how the character reacts to the problem.

Key Questions:

- What problem or problems did this character face?

- How did he or she respond to them? Was the response appropriate? Successful?

- How would you have handled the situation?

Usage Notes: Emphasize this type of analysis as a way for students to learn valuable lessons they can apply in their own lives.

LC-5: A Character's Family Tree

Objective: Students will create a family tree for a character.

Key Questions:

- Who are the character's relatives?

- Why are these relationships important to the story?

- Which relationship seems most important? Why?

Usage Notes: Use this graphic organizer with appropriate, family-based stories.

LC-6: Character Constellation

Objective: Students will create a graphic organizer that depicts the characters in a story and the relationships among them.

Key Questions:

- Why is it important to understand *all* of these relationships?

- Are some relationships more important to the story than others? How so?

- How do relationships change during the course of this story? How do you indicate such changes in a character constellation?

Usage Notes: Make sure students understand the mechanics of this type of graphic organizer, especially using and labeling arrows. Students can expand their graphic organizers by jotting down a few key character traits in each character's circle.

LC-7: Comparing and Contrasting Characters

Objective: Students will compare and contrast two literary characters.

Key Questions:

- Which traits are unique to each character?

- Which traits do the characters have in common?

Usage Notes: Students can compare and contrast two characters from the same story or similar characters from different stories. Make sure students understand that each trait should appear only once, in only one area of the Venn diagram.

LC-8: Comparing Yourself to a Character

Objective: Students will compare and contrast themselves with a character in literature.

Key Questions:

- How are you similar to this character?

- How are you different from this character?

- What can you learn about yourself by comparing and contrasting yourself with a character?

Usage Notes: Be careful to respect students' privacy. Make sure students understand that each trait should appear only once, in only one area of the Venn diagram.

Name _____ Date _____

L-1: What Is Literature?

Introduction: What exactly does **literature** mean? If "story" comes to mind, you're on the right track. Literature includes stories, but not all stories are literature. Literature has a precise meaning. You'll study literature throughout your school career and enjoy it for the rest of your life. This activity will help you understand what literature really means.

• **Directions:** Complete the graphic organizer.

Writing the Book on Literature

Taking Another Step: Compare what you wrote under "Literature that I have enjoyed" with what a friend wrote. Make a pact with your friend to read something new from each other's list.

Name _____ Date _____ | **Student Activity Sheet** |

L-2: An Author Profile

Introduction: When you are reading good literature, it's easy to get lost in the story and really enjoy what you read. But if you especially like what you are reading, you would probably enjoy finding out about whoever wrote it. Authors can be truly fascinating individuals. In fact, some of the most interesting, important, and influential people in history have been authors. In this activity, you'll create a biographical profile to learn more about one of your favorite authors.

• **Directions:** Conduct research to complete the chart below.

The Life and Work of an Author	
Name	
Life dates	
Where author lived and worked (country, city, etc.)	
Major works	
Important contributions to literature	
Interesting personal information	
Why I like this author	
Additional information	

Taking Another Step: If this author is still alive, write a letter explaining what you like about his or her work and asking any questions you'd like. A librarian can help you find the correct address for the letter.

Name _____ Date _____ | **Student Activity Sheet** |

L-3: A Book Summary

Introduction: Summarizing a book is a good way to remember its main events and ideas and how they fit together.

• **Directions:** Write the chapter number, title, and the main events and ideas for each chapter below.

Book Title: _____

Author: _____

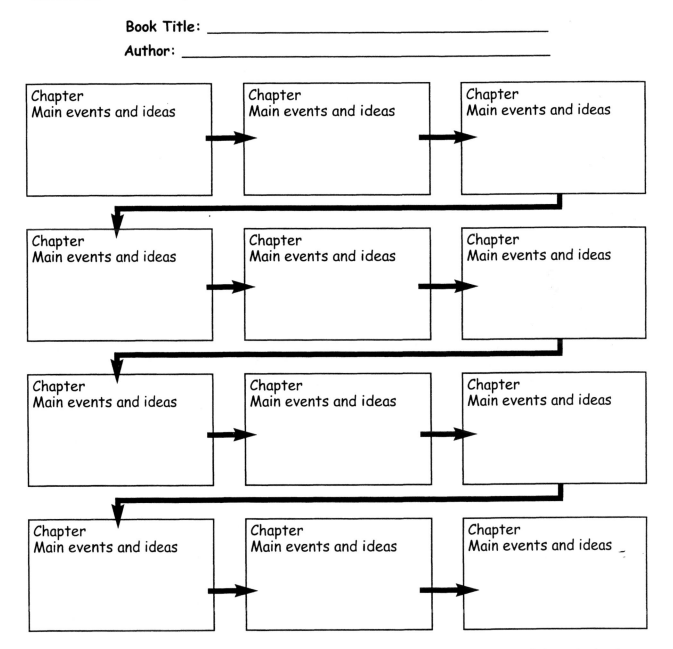

Taking Another Step: Use the chapter summaries to write a one-paragraph summary of the entire book.

Name _____ Date _____

LS-1: What Is Setting?

Introduction: The setting of a story is one of its basic features. To enjoy and even to understand any piece of literature, you need to know its setting. This activity helps you discover what setting means in literature.

• **Directions:** Complete the graphic organizer below.

Definition of Setting

How you can tell what the setting is

Why you need to know the setting of a story

How the setting can affect the plot of a story

Taking Another Step: On the back of this sheet, write a brief description of the setting of a story you have recently read.

24   *Graphic Organizers for Language Arts Classes*

Name _____ Date _____

LS-2: The Setting of a Story

Introduction: You can describe the setting of anything that ever happened by identifying *when* and *where* it happened. One is not enough—you need both. An event's setting is its time (when) and its place (where). The setting of a story is also time and place. Stories often have more than one setting, but each setting has a time and a place. In this activity, you will see how these two characteristics define the setting of a story—it's as easy as 1 1 1!

• **Directions:** Complete the graphic organizer to "calculate" the setting of a story. Be sure to explain how you know each thing that you write down.

Adding up the setting of _____
(*story title*)

TIME

When the story takes place:

How I know this is:

PLACE

Where the story takes place:

How I know this is:

+

THE SETTING IS:

=

Taking Another Step: Was it easier for you to determine the time or the place of the setting? Why? Write your answer on the back of this sheet.

Name _____ Date _____

LS-3: Piecing Together the Setting of a Story

Introduction: When you describe the setting of a story, you identify its time and place. For example, the setting of *To Kill a Mockingbird* is a small southern town (place) during the 1930's (time). But usually, the author doesn't tell you this directly. You have to figure out the setting of a story for yourself, using clues from the story. For example, how the characters speak may reveal that they are from a certain part of the country (a place clue). Or, they may ride horses instead of driving cars (a time clue.) By putting together several place clues and several time clues, you can figure out the setting of a story.

• **Directions:** Complete the graphic organizer to show how you "pieced together" the setting of a story.

The Setting of _____

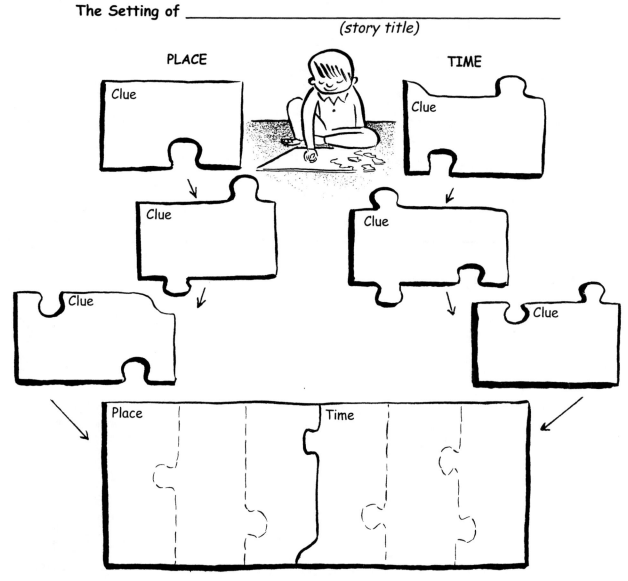

Taking Another Step: When you use clues to figure something out, you are **making an inference**. Besides setting, what else can you figure out in a story by making inferences? Write your answer on the back of this sheet.

Name _____ Date _____

LP-1: What Is Plot?

Introduction: A story wouldn't be a story without a plot. The most basic definition of **plot** is simply the sequence of events that takes place in a literary work. But, like many terms used to discuss literature, plot has many aspects. Since the plot is so important in any piece of literature, understanding what the word "plot" actually means is crucial to getting the most out of your reading. This activity helps you do just that.

• **Directions:** Complete the graphic organizer by answering each question inside the letters.

What is a "plot"?

What are the major parts of a plot?

Why is a plot so important?

Why is it important for you to follow and understand the plot of a story?

Taking Another Step: Use a dictionary to find out where the word *plot* comes from. Explain the word's origin and development in a paragraph on the back of this sheet.

Name _____ Date _____

LP-2: Mapping a Plot

Introduction: In most stories, the plot follows the same basic pattern. The **exposition** introduces, or exposes, readers to the setting, characters, conflict, and other things they need to know. As the plot advances, events in the story rise toward a **climax**. This process is called **rising action**. After the crisis, the **falling action** of the plot leads to a **resolution** of the conflict in the plot. To help you see how all of these elements fit together, you can summarize a story in a plot map.

• **Directions:** Complete the plot map by filling in important events from a story in the correct boxes. Cross out any boxes you don't need.

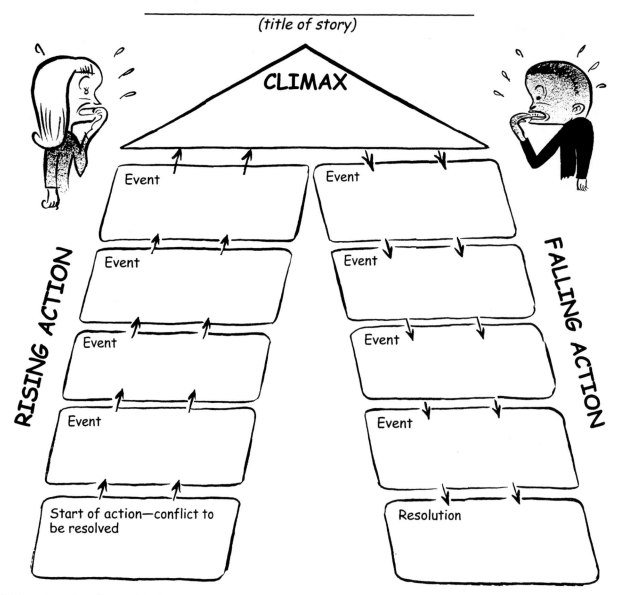

_____
(title of story)

CLIMAX

RISING ACTION

FALLING ACTION

Event

Event

Event

Event

Event

Event

Event

Event

Start of action—conflict to be resolved

Resolution

Taking Another Step: Find out what the word *denouement* means and explain how it is related to the steps in a plot. Write your answer on the back of this sheet.

28   *Graphic Organizers for Language Arts Classes*

Name _____ Date _____

LP-3: Plot and Subplots

Introduction: The prefix *sub-* means "under" or "inferior to." So, a *sub*marine travels under water, and a *sub*committee is inferior to the main committee of which it is a part. In literature, we frequently use the term *subplot*. A subplot is simply a plot that is "under" or "inferior to" the main plot in a story. It may be related to the main plot, but it is not the main plot. Authors use subplots to make their stories more interesting, fun, and realistic. The diagram on this page shows you how to follow subplots.

• **Directions:** Complete the diagram by writing a few sentences that summarize the main plot in the center box. Then summarize each subplot in an oval. In the diamond, explain how the subplot is related to the main plot. These relationships may involve characters, events, or both—be as specific as you can. Cross out any parts of the diagram that you don't need.

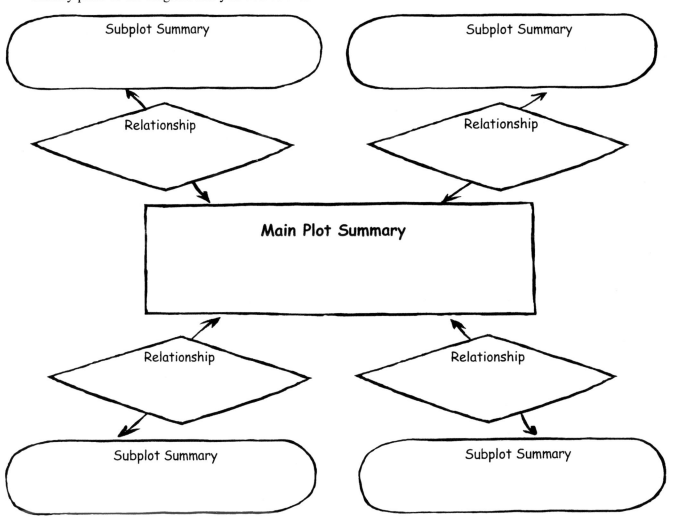

Taking Another Step: Do you think the subplots add to the main plot or distract from it? Explain your answer on the back of this sheet.

Name _____ Date _____ | **Student Activity Sheet**

LP-4: Answering Questions About an Event in a Plot

Introduction: Follow this logic: A story has a plot, and a plot is a series of events. So, to understand a story, it makes sense that you have to understand each event. Unfortunately, sometimes readers miss important events as they race through a story. As you are reading, sometimes you need to slow down and think about specific events. Answering some basic questions about each event in the plot helps you understand the whole story.

• **Directions:** Identify the event that you are going to focus on in the center box. Then answer each question about the event.

Story Title: _____

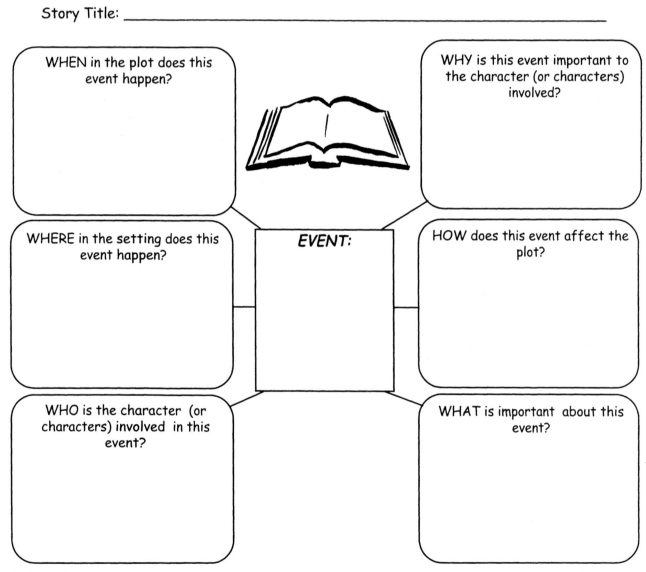

WHEN in the plot does this event happen?

WHY is this event important to the character (or characters) involved?

WHERE in the setting does this event happen?

EVENT:

HOW does this event affect the plot?

WHO is the character (or characters) involved in this event?

WHAT is important about this event?

Taking Another Step: Using your diagram, write a one-paragraph summary of the event and its importance to the story. Write your paragraph on the back of this page.

Name _____ Date _____ | **Student Activity Sheet**

LP-5: A Circle Map of a Story

Introduction: Good writing gives you a feeling of wholeness or completeness. Upon finishing the story, you have a sense of satisfaction. Writers often accomplish this by ending the story where it began. Of course, the situation isn't the same. The events of the plot have changed the situation, and the characters have changed in some way. But, many stories either finish in the same setting where they started, or end by referring to something that happened at the beginning of the story. Along with the characters, the reader has gone "full circle." So, a circle is a good way to draw a map of a story—and it can help you see why you have that feeling of satisfaction that only comes from a good story.

• **Directions:** Complete the circle map by listing the major events in the story in order, clockwise. If your teacher asks you to, label each event as part of the rising action, as the climax, as part of the falling action, or as the resolution. Cross out any part of the circle that you don't need.

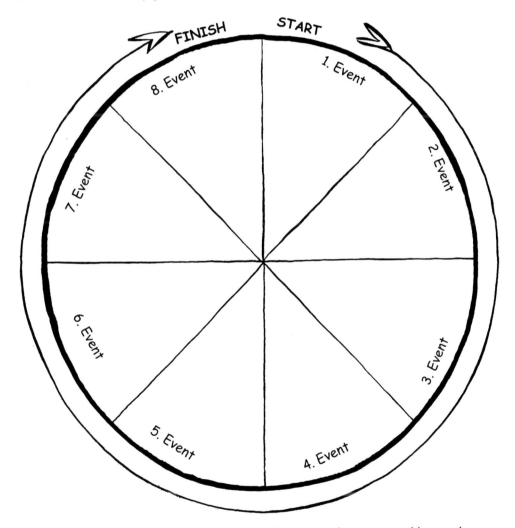

Taking Another Step: Write a paragraph on the back of this page that answers this question: How does the author take the reader "full circle" in this story, and why?

Name _____ Date _____

LP-6: A Storyboard

Introduction: Think about the last television show you watched. How many different scenes were there? Probably a lot—a half-hour show may have a dozen or more scenes. The people who make television shows plan each scene with what is called a **storyboard**. A storyboard is a series of sketches that shows the "story" on a "board" (like a bulletin board). Each sketch is a rough drawing of the major event of one scene. Brief written notes about what takes place in the scene accompany each sketch. Arranging the sketches and notes in order provides a good summary of the television show. You can use this storyboard technique to summarize a book or a story.

• **Directions:** Use the diagram below to make a storyboard for something you have read. In each box, sketch what happens in a main "scene," or event, in the story. Beneath each sketch, write a brief, one- or two-sentence note about what happens in that scene.

Story Title: _____

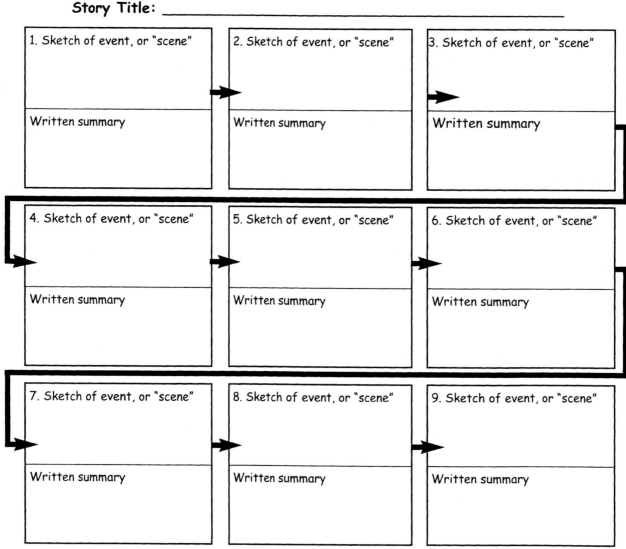

Name _____ Date _____

LP-7: Events/Decision Chain

Introduction: The plot of a story doesn't advance by itself. Something happens to move the story ahead. Maybe a volcano erupts, or a rainbow appears. But usually, what makes the plot advance is *decisions* made by the characters. For example, a character might decide to travel someplace, or decide to confront another character, or decide to leave a job. Such decisions lead to events that make up the plot and eventually the story. Here's how to see the relationship between the characters' decisions and plot development in a story.

• **Directions:** Complete the diagram by listing key events in a story. Between each event, identify what decision led to the next event, who made the decision, and why.

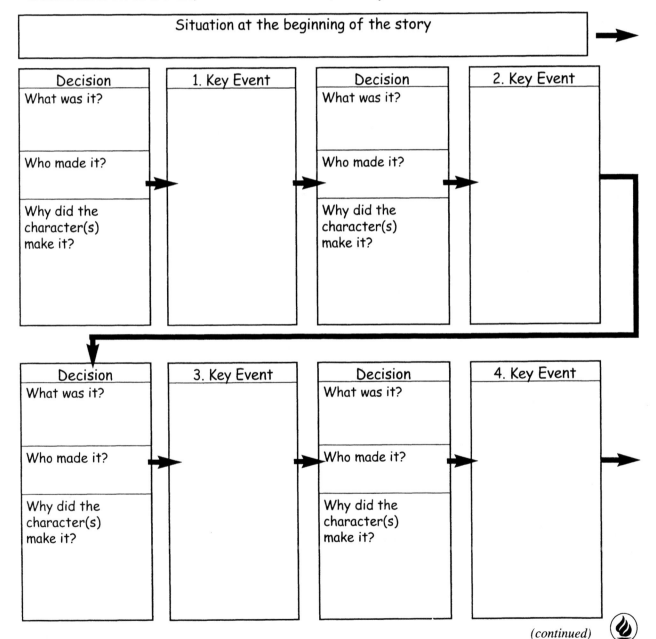

Situation at the beginning of the story

Decision	1. Key Event	Decision	2. Key Event
What was it?		What was it?	
Who made it?		Who made it?	
Why did the character(s) make it?		Why did the character(s) make it?	

Decision	3. Key Event	Decision	4. Key Event
What was it?		What was it?	
Who made it?		Who made it?	
Why did the character(s) make it?		Why did the character(s) make it?	

(continued)

33 *Graphic Organizers for Language Arts Classes*

Name _____ Date _____

LP-7: Events/Decision Chain *(continued)*

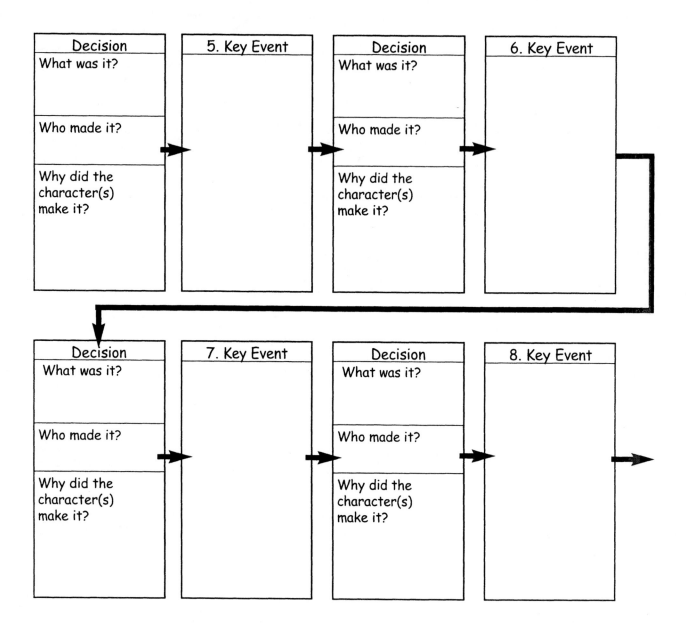

Decision	5. Key Event	Decision	6. Key Event
What was it?		What was it?	
Who made it?		Who made it?	
Why did the character(s) make it?		Why did the character(s) make it?	

Decision	7. Key Event	Decision	8. Key Event
What was it?		What was it?	
Who made it?		Who made it?	
Why did the character(s) make it?		Why did the character(s) make it?	

Taking Another Step: On the back of this sheet, describe an important decision you have made in your own life and the event or events that resulted from your decision.

Name _____ Date _____

LC-1: Major Character Traits

Introduction: Some of the most wonderful—and worst!—people you'll ever meet are the characters in stories you read. You can get to know them better by thinking about their traits. **Traits** are characteristics, the things that make one person different from another. **Physical traits** are how someone appears. **Mental traits** are how someone thinks. **Social traits** are how someone interacts with others. **Emotional traits** are how someone feels. **Main characteristics** are those that seem to dominate others.

• **Directions:** Complete the organizer by listing as many traits about a character in each category as you can.

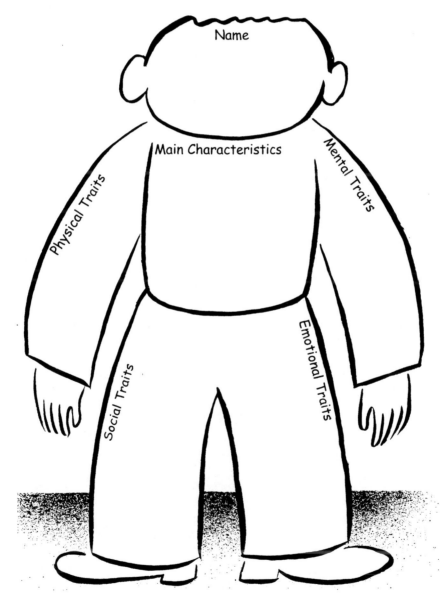

Taking Another Step: Do you like this character? Why or why not? Explain on the back of this sheet.

35   *Graphic Organizers for Language Arts Classes*

Name _____ Date _____

LC-2: Clues About a Character

Introduction: Often, instead of telling you what a character is like, the author only gives you **clues**. For example, if a character pets a dog, then rescues a cat from a tree, you can figure out from these clues that this character is kind to animals. Figuring out what a character is like from clues is one of the most enjoyable things about reading. To get to "know" a character, use the diagram on this page.

• **Directions:** In each box on the left-hand side, list one of the character's traits. In each box on the right-hand side, list the clue or clues that let readers know that the character has the trait.

Name of Character: _____

I know the character has each of these traits . . .   **. . . because of these clues.**

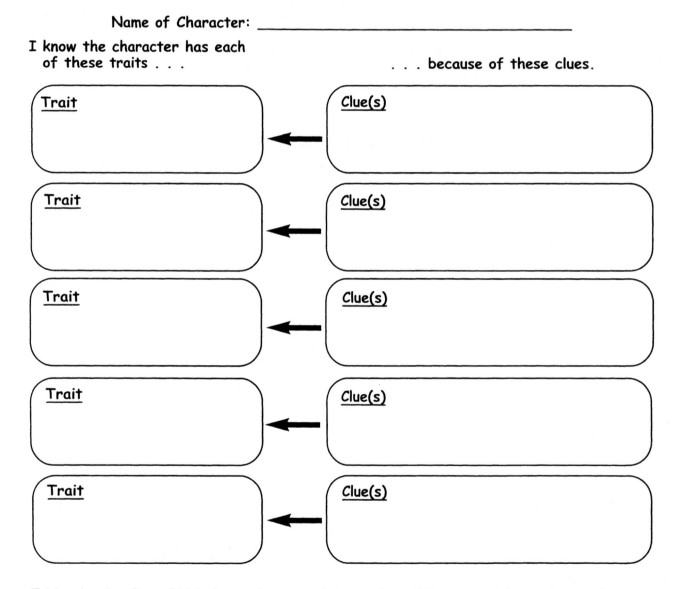

Taking Another Step: Think about a character trait that you have. What clues might let other people know that you have that trait?

36   *Graphic Organizers for Language Arts Classes*

Name _____ Date _____

LC-3: A Character Circle Graph

Introduction: Is there someone you think of as a "nice" person? As a "neat" person? As an "always running late" person? How about someone who is all of the above—nice, neat, and always running late? The truth is that no person, and no character in literature, has just one trait. Characters have many traits that, taken together, make them who they are. However, some traits are more important than others. For example, if a character is nice, that is probably more important than always running late. But, if someone gets hurt because of running late, then the "running late" trait becomes more important. Putting a character's different traits in a circle graph is a good way to think about how important they are.

• **Directions:** Study the example. Then make a circle graph that shows the traits of a character that you choose. Divide the circle into different-size wedges. The more important the trait is to the story, the larger the wedge should be. Be sure to label each wedge.

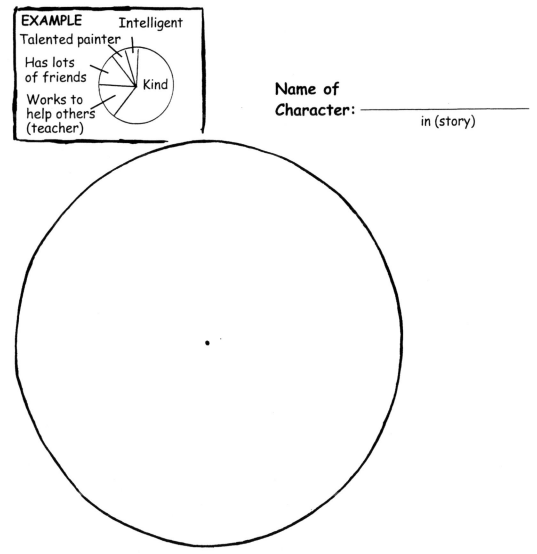

Name of
Character: _____
                        in (story)

Taking Another Step: Make a similar circle graph that shows your own character traits.

Name _____ Date _____

LC-4: A Character's Problem and Solution

Introduction: One of the most important reasons that people read literature is to learn things that improve their own lives. For example, you might read a story about a young girl who is fighting with her mother. By reading about how she solves this problem, you could get some ideas about how to avoid or solve a similar problem in your own life. The flow chart on this page will help you focus on how a character in a story that you've read faced and solved a problem.

• **Directions:** Write the title of the story below. Then, complete each box in the flow chart.

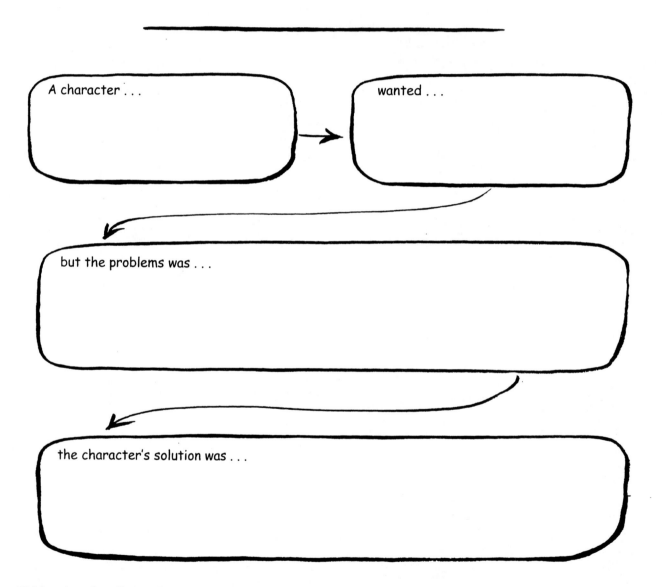

A character . . .

wanted . . .

but the problems was . . .

the character's solution was . . .

Taking Another Step: On the back of this sheet, write a paragraph about something you've learned from reading a story that has helped in your own life.

Name _____ Date _____

LC-5: A Character's Family Tree

Introduction: In stories with many characters, it is sometimes difficult to keep all of them straight. (If you're from a very large family, you might have the same problem in real life!) A good way to keep track of all of the characters is making a family tree.

• **Directions:** Complete the family tree for the main character in a story. Add branches as you need them.

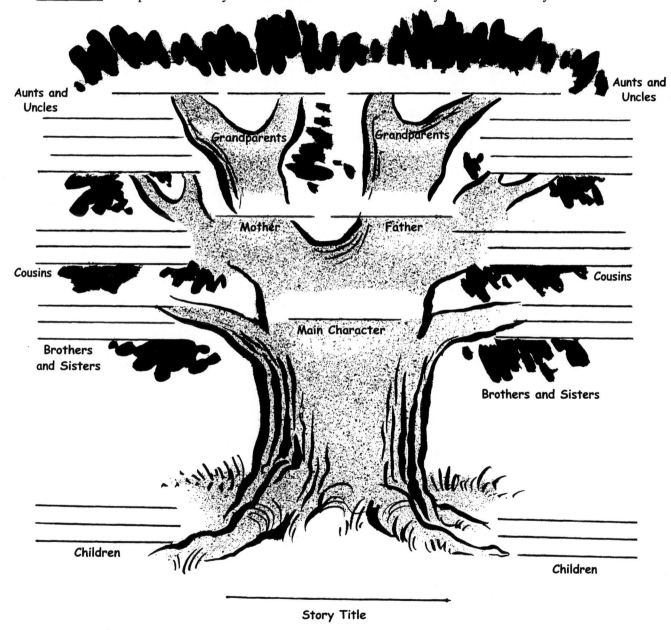

Taking Another Step: Explain why family relationships are so important to this story. Use the back of this sheet.

Name _____ Date _____

LC-6: A Character Constellation

Introduction: A "character constellation" is a diagram that shows the relationships among characters in a story. Each character is represented by a circle. Lines and arrows between the circles represent the relationships between characters. In the sample below, the character José likes the character Melinda.

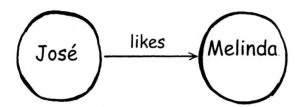

Another line and arrow show how Melinda feels about José: She doesn't like him back!

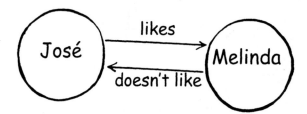

Ken is another character in the story. As you can see, he and José are friends. Ken doesn't know Melinda, so there are no arrows between them.

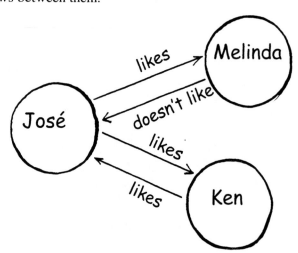

You can expand diagrams like this to include every character and every relationship in a story. Just be sure to draw the arrows and label them with the correct feelings. Note that your choices are not limited to "like" and "doesn't like." Other possibilities include "fears," "loves," "hates," "is concerned about," and so on—whatever best describes the relationship.

• **Directions:** On the next page, draw a character constellation for a story.

(continued)

Name _____ Date _____

LC-6: A Character Constellation *(continued)*

A Character Constellation of _____
(title)

Taking Another Step: Draw a character constellation of the people in your own life on the back of this page.

Name _____ Date _____

LC-7: Comparing and Contrasting Characters

Introduction: Like people in real life, the characters in a story are alike in some ways and different in others. You can identify how two characters are both alike and different using two intersecting circles.

• **Directions:** Compare and contrast two characters. Write the names of the characters on the lines provided. Under each name, list the traits that make that character different from the other. Where the circles overlap, list the traits that both characters have.

Comparing and Contrasting Two Characters from _____
(title)

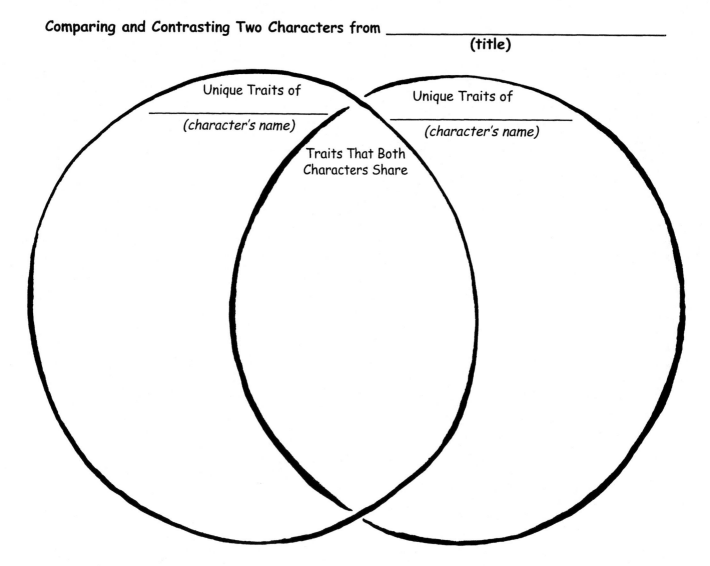

Unique Traits of

_____
(character's name)

Unique Traits of

_____
(character's name)

Traits That Both
Characters Share

Taking Another Step: Explain how this diagram helps you understand and explain the relationship between these two characters in the story.

Name _____ Date _____

LC-8: Comparing Yourself to a Character

Introduction: Have you ever read a story and really identified with a character? Have you found that a character is like you in some important way? Comparing yourself with people you read about is a great way to learn some valuable things about yourself—and maybe even learn how to become a better person.

• **Directions:** In the circle labeled "Me," list some of your most important traits. In the circle labeled "Character," write the character's name on the line and then list some of the character's most important traits. Where the circles overlap, under "Both of Us," list the traits you and the character share. Each trait should appear in only one of the three areas.

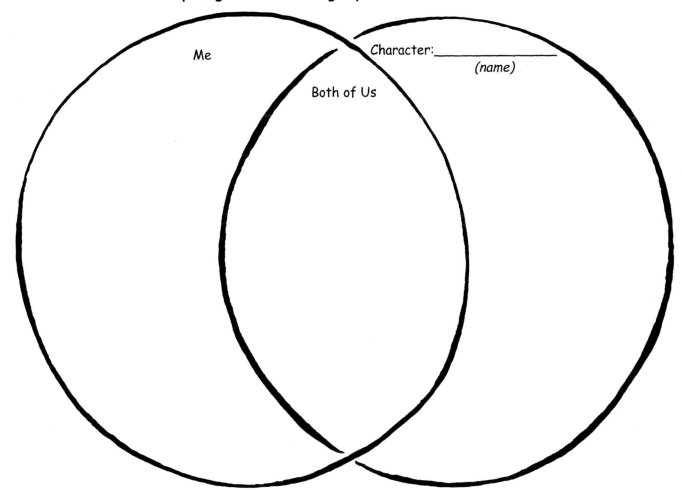

Comparing and Contrasting Myself with a Character

Me

Character:_____
(name)

Both of Us

Taking Another Step: In a paragraph, tell about the character you have "met" through reading that you admire the most. What do you like about him or her? How could you become more like this character? Write your paragraph on the back of this page.

III.   Composition: The Writing Process

These graphic organizers are based on the four-step model of the writing process: prewriting, drafting, revising, and publishing. Consider assigning them in sequence in conjunction with a student writing assignment.

C-1: Steps in the Writing Process

Objective: Students will identify and describe each step in the writing process.

Key Questions:
- What does "writing is a process" mean?
- What are the steps in the writing process?
- What is involved in each step?
- Why are these steps important and useful?

Usage Notes: Encourage students to memorize the steps and understand the concept of process in this context. Explain how the steps can overlap.

> *Answers:*
> Step 1. Prewriting: Deciding on a subject, gathering information, and putting your ideas in order
> Step 2. Drafting: putting your ideas into written sentences and adding new ideas
> Step 3. Revising: Making changes in content and organization to improve your draft
> Step 4. Publishing: Eliminating minor errors and presenting your finished paper

C-2: The Writing Process

Step 1, Prewriting

Objective: Students will explore the prewriting step of the writing process.

Key Questions:
- What are some examples of your use of prewriting?
- Why is prewriting important?
- Questions formed from headings in the graphic organizer

Usage Notes: Emphasize this step as fundamental to the idea that writing is an ongoing process, and not a single act. Explain how prewriting can help save time and avoid frustration later on.

C-3: The Writing Process

Step 2, Drafting

Objective: Students will explore the drafting step of the writing process.

Key Questions:

- What are some examples of your use of drafting techniques?

- Why is drafting important?

- Questions formed from headings in the graphic organizer

Usage Notes: Emphasize that this step is fundamental to the idea that writing is an ongoing process, not a single act.

C-4: The Writing Process

Step 3, Revising

Objective: Students will explore the revising step of the writing process.

Key Questions:

- What are some examples of your use of revising techniques?

- Why is revising important?

- Questions formed from headings in the graphic organizer

Usage Notes: Emphasize that this step is arguably the most important in the writing process—the one that deserves the most time in a writing assignment.

C-5: The Writing Process

Step 4, Publishing

Objective: Students will explore the publishing step of the writing process.

Key Questions:

- What are some examples of how you might publish your paper?

- Why is publishing important?

- Questions formed from headings in the graphic organizer

Usage Notes: Explain proofreading and proofreading techniques to students.

Name _____ Date _____

C-1: Steps in the Writing Process

Introduction: Memorize the following statement, and you will save yourself years of frustration, hard work, and poor grades: *Writing is not an act—writing is a process.*

What it means is that writing is not a single action. You just don't sit down and write. Writing is a **process**, or a series of steps, and you only need to take one step at a time. There are only **four steps**, which makes writing as easy as 1-2-3—okay, 1-2-3-4!

• **Directions:** The names and descriptions of the four steps in the writing process are listed in random order in the box. Copy them in the **correct locations** on the staircase.

Scrambled Steps in the Writing Process

NAME OF STEP	DESCRIPTION
Drafting	making changes in content and organization to improve your draft
Publishing	deciding on a subject, gathering information, and putting your ideas in order
Revising	putting your ideas into written sentences and adding new ideas
Prewriting	eliminating minor errors and presenting your finished paper

---

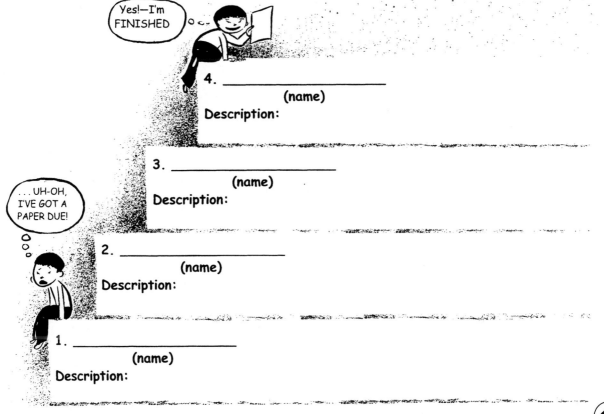

Yes!—I'm FINISHED

4. _____
　　　　　　(name)
Description:

3. _____
　　　　　　(name)
Description:

. . . UH-OH, I'VE GOT A PAPER DUE!

2. _____
　　　　　　(name)
Description:

1. _____
　　　　　　(name)
Description:

　　　　49　　　　*Graphic Organizers for Language Arts Classes*

Name _____ Date _____

C-2: The Writing Process
Step 1, Prewriting

Introduction: The first step in the writing process is **prewriting**. *Pre* means "before," so prewriting is what you do before you actually start to write.

• **Directions:** Learn about prewriting by filling in the bricks in the bottom step below.

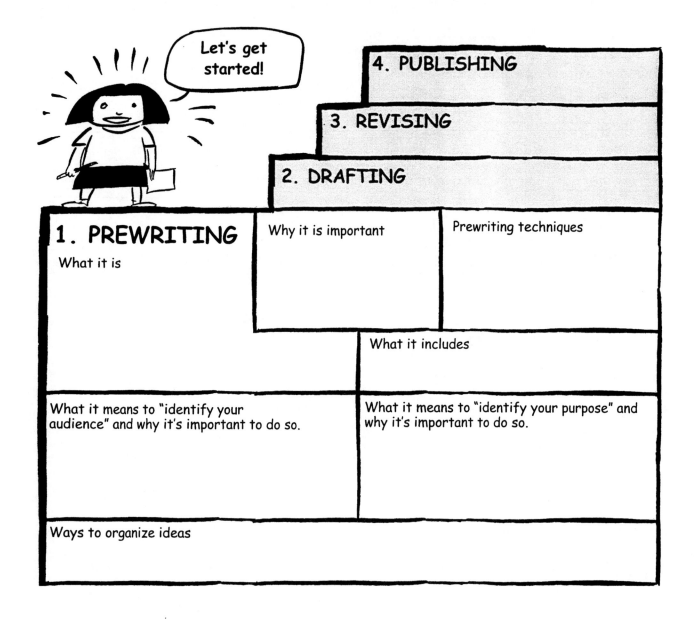

Name _____ Date _____

C-3: The Writing Process
Step 2, Drafting

Introduction: The second step in the writing process is **drafting**. It is no more and no less important than other steps. Drafting is, however, when you first put pen to paper (or fingers to keyboard), and your writing really begins to take shape.

• **Directions:** Learn about drafting by filling in the bricks in the second step.

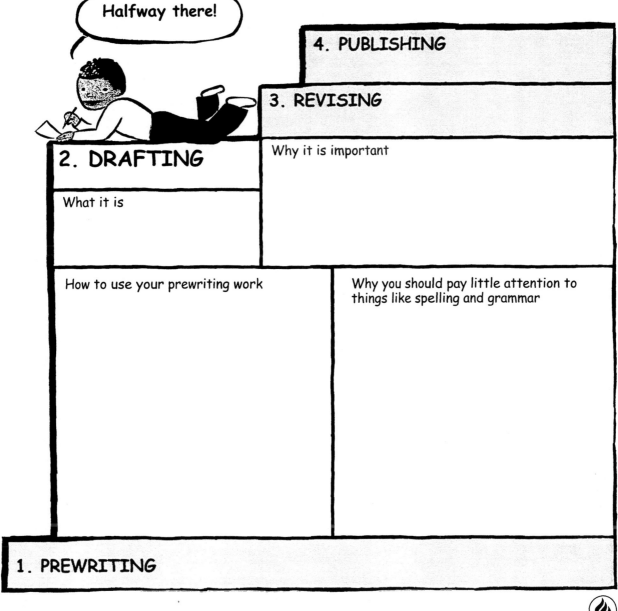

Name _____ Date _____

C-4: The Writing Process
Step 3, Revising

Introduction: The third step in the writing process is **revising**. Every good writer knows that revising is essential. One writer said that revising is the heart of the writing process. Why? The answer is that revising makes you focus on how well you are saying what you have decided to say. It is when whatever you are writing takes on its final form. *In fact, you should probably take more time revising your writing than you take on any other step!* Think of revising as "pausing" on the staircase!

• **Directions:** Learn about revising by filling in the bricks in the third step.

> I can make it better!!

4. PUBLISHING

3. REVISING

What it is

Why it's important

Techniques for revising style

Techniques for revising organization

Techniques for revising content

2. DRAFTING

1. PREWRITING

52   *Graphic Organizers for Language Arts Classes*

Name _____ Date _____

C-5: The Writing Process
Step 4, Publishing

Introduction: The last step in the writing process is **publishing**. A better term for it might be "proofreading and publishing," because you should definitely proofread your paper before you publish it.

• **Directions:** Learn about proofreading and publishing by filling in the bricks in the top step.

4. PUBLISHING

What publishing is

Ways to publish

What proofreading is

Proofreading techniques

3. REVISING

2. DRAFTING

1. PREWRITING

IV. Grammar: The Sentence and the Parts of Speech

These graphic organizers emphasize learning and memorizing fundamental facts about sentences and the parts of speech and associated ideas.
Consider having students assemble the Parts of Speech graphic organizers
into grammar portfolios.

G-1: What Is Grammar?

Objective: Students will explore some fundamental ideas about grammar.

Key Questions:
- What is grammar?
- Why is it important?

Usage Notes: Emphasize good grammar as a vital life skill.

G-2: The Sentence

Objective: Students will explore the sentence by defining it and listing some of its important aspects.

Key Questions:
- What is a sentence?
- What does every sentence begin and end with?
- What are the parts of a sentence?
- What are the four types of sentences?

Usage Notes: Encourage students to memorize the information in the graphic organizer.

G-3: The Parts of Speech

Objective: Students will identify and define the eight parts of speech.

Key Questions:
- What are the eight parts of speech?
- What is the definition of each?
- What is an example of each?
- Why is it important to know the eight parts of speech?

Usage Notes: Encourage students to memorize the information in the graphic organizer.

G-4: The Noun

Objective: Students will define, explain, and explore important ideas about nouns.

Key Questions:

• What are nouns?

• Questions formed from the headings in the graphic organizer

Usage Notes: Encourage students to memorize the information in the graphic organizer.

G-5: The Pronoun

Objective: Students will define, explain, and explore important ideas about pronouns.

Key Questions:

• What are pronouns?

• Questions formed from the headings in the graphic organizer

Usage Notes: Encourage students to memorize the information in the graphic organizer.

G-6: The Adjective

Objective: Students will define, explain, and explore important ideas about adjectives.

Key Questions:

• What are adjectives?

• Questions formed from the headings in the graphic organizer

Usage Notes: Encourage students to memorize the information in the graphic organizer.

G-7: The Verb

Objective: Students will define, explain, and explore important ideas about verbs.

Key Questions:

• What are verbs?

• Questions formed from the headings in the graphic organizer

Usage Notes: Encourage students to memorize the information in the graphic organizer.

G-8: The Adverb

Objective: Students will define, explain, and explore important ideas about adverbs.

Key Questions:

- What are adverbs?

- Questions formed from the headings in the graphic organizer

Usage Notes: Encourage students to memorize the information in the graphic organizer.

G-9: The Preposition

Objective: Students will define, explain, and explore important ideas about prepositions and prepositional phrases.

Key Questions:

- What are prepositions?

- Questions formed from the headings in the graphic organizer

Usage Notes: Encourage students to memorize the information in the graphic organizer.

G-10: The Conjunction

Objective: Students will define, explain, and explore important ideas about conjunctions.

Key Questions:

- What are conjunctions?

- Questions formed from the headings in the graphic organizer

Usage Notes: Encourage students to memorize the information in the graphic organizer.

G-11: The Interjection

Objective: Students will define, explain, and explore important ideas about interjections.

Key Questions:

- What are interjections?

- Questions formed from the headings in the graphic organizer

Usage Notes: Encourage students to memorize the information in the graphic organizer.

Name _____ Date _____

G-1: What Is Grammar?

Introduction: Whether you know it or not, people judge you by your grammar. Using **good grammar** when you speak and when you write sends a message to other people. It marks you as an educated and thoughtful person. Perhaps more important, using good grammar will help you communicate effectively. People will understand you better. Think about how important this is as you complete the diagram below.

• **Directions:** Complete the diagram by answering each question.

Grammar Is Important!

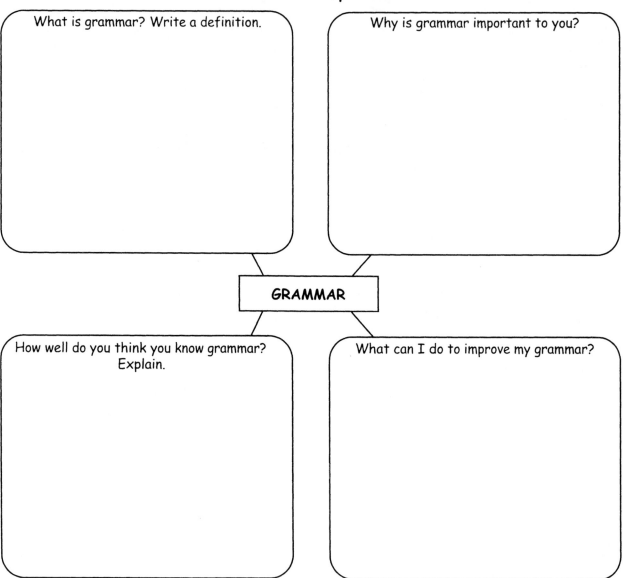

What is grammar? Write a definition.

Why is grammar important to you?

GRAMMAR

How well do you think you know grammar? Explain.

What can I do to improve my grammar?

Taking Another Step: On the back of this sheet, complete this sentence: "Good grammar is important because . . ."

Name _____ Date _____

G-2: The Sentence

Introduction: Nothing is as basic to your study of English as the **sentence**. After all, the purpose of language is to communicate, and the sentence is the basic way that we express a complete idea. The diagram on this page will teach you most of what you need to know about the sentence.

• **Directions:** Complete the diagram.

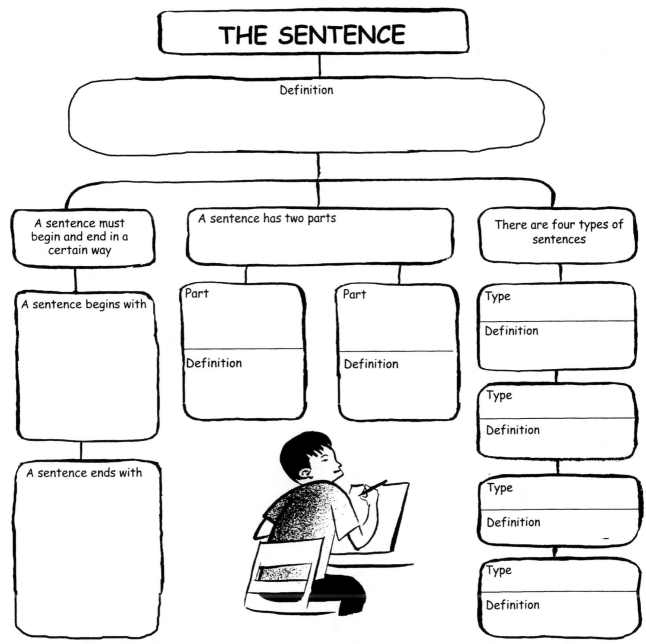

Taking Another Step: Why is it important for you to know how to write correct, clear sentences? Write your answer on the back of this sheet.

©1998 J. Weston Walch, Publisher 61 *Graphic Organizers for Language Arts Classes*

Name _____ Date _____

G-3: The Parts of Speech

Introduction: A lot of students think of grammar as somewhat "creepy." That's one way to help remember one of the most basic things about grammar: the **parts of speech**. In English, there are **eight** parts of speech. Spiders have eight legs. And because most people also think spiders are somewhat "creepy," here's an easy way to remember the parts of speech.

• **Directions:** Complete the diagram by identifying the eight parts of speech and writing their definitions.

Taking Another Step: Another way to help you remember the eight parts of speech is to make up a silly sentence in which each word begins with the first letter of one of the parts of speech. Make up such a silly sentence and write it down on the back of this sheet.

       Graphic Organizers for Language Arts Classes

Name _____ Date _____

G-4: The Noun

Directions: The **noun** is one of the eight parts of speech. Learn about nouns by completing the diagram.

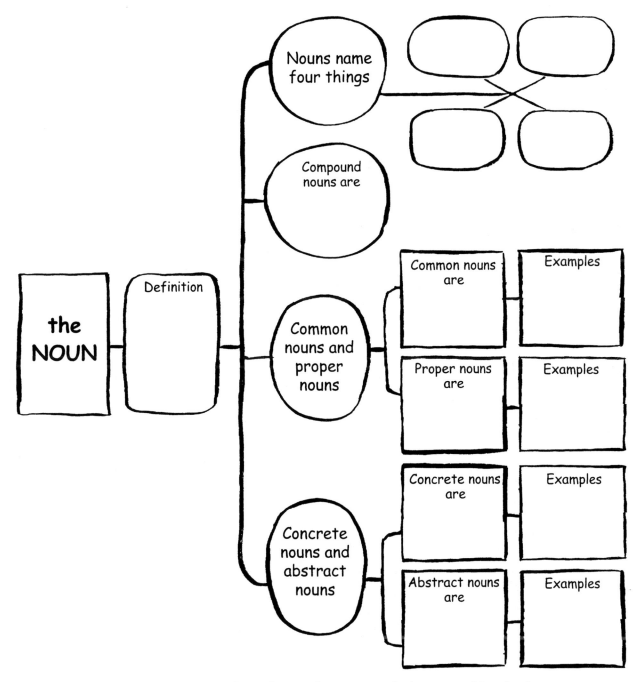

Taking Another Step: On the back of this sheet, write a paragraph about something that interests you, or copy a paragraph from a book. Make a list of all of the nouns in the paragraph. Identify what each noun is naming and what type or types of noun it is.

Name _____ Date _____ | **Student Activity Sheet**

G-5: The Pronoun

• **Directions:** The **pronoun** is one of the eight parts of speech. Learn about pronouns by completing the diagram.

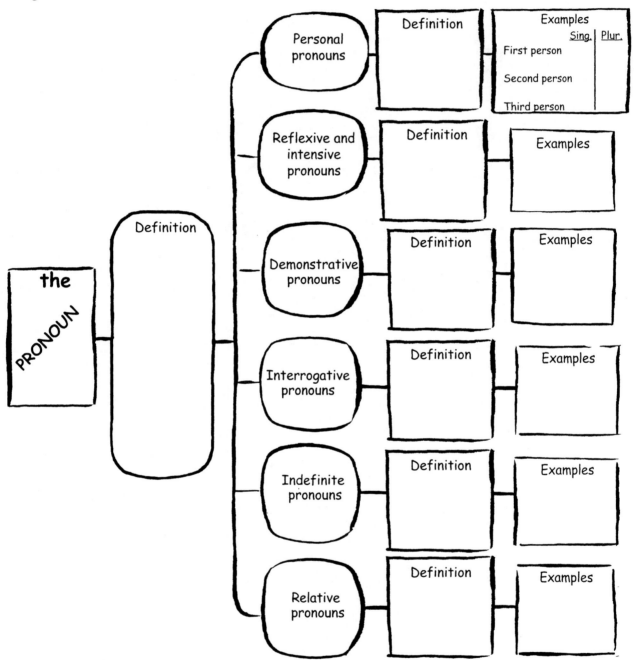

Taking Another Step: On the back of this sheet, write a paragraph about something you did with a friend or a group of friends. Make a list of all of the pronouns in the paragraph. Identify what type or types of pronoun each one is.

Name _____ Date _____

G-6: The Adjective

• **Directions:** The **adjective** is one of the eight parts of speech. Learn about adjectives by completing the diagram.

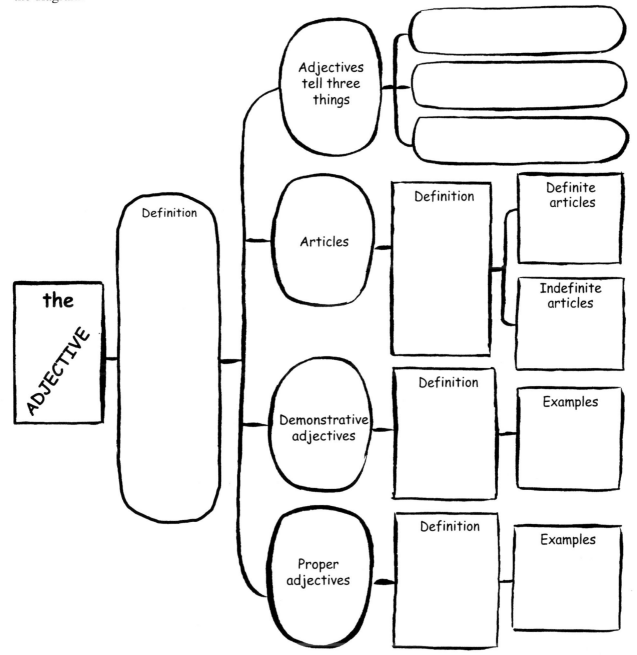

Taking Another Step: On the back of this sheet, write a paragraph about something that interests you, or copy a paragraph from a book. Make a list of all of the adjectives in the paragraph. Identify what type or types of adjective each one is.

Name _____ Date _____

G-7: The Verb

• **Directions:** The **verb** is one of the eight parts of speech. Learn about verbs by completing the diagram.

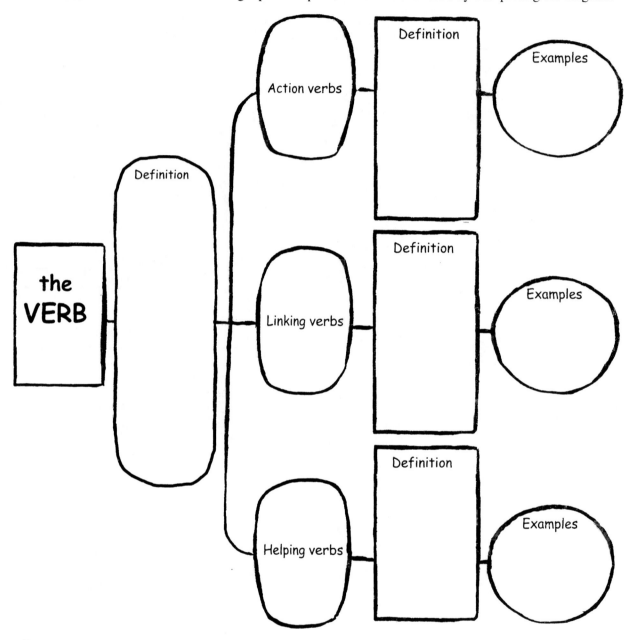

Taking Another Step: On the back of this sheet, write a paragraph about something that interests you, or copy a paragraph from a book. Make a list of all of the verbs in the paragraph. Identify what type or types of verb each one is.

Name _____ Date _____

G-8: The Adverb

• **<u>Directions:</u>** The **adverb** is one of the eight parts of speech. Learn about adverbs by completing the diagram.

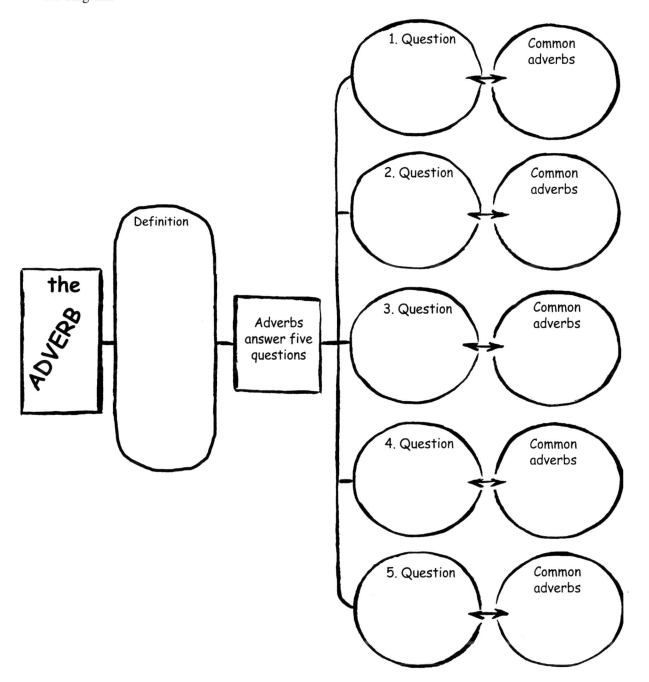

the ADVERB

Definition

Adverbs answer five questions

1. Question — Common adverbs

2. Question — Common adverbs

3. Question — Common adverbs

4. Question — Common adverbs

5. Question — Common adverbs

<u>Taking Another Step:</u> On the back of this sheet, write a paragraph about something that interests you, or copy a paragraph from a book. Make a list of all of the adverbs in the paragraph. Identify which question each adverb answers.

Name _____ Date _____

G-9: The Preposition

• **Directions:** The **preposition** is one of the eight parts of speech. Learn about prepositions by completing the diagram.

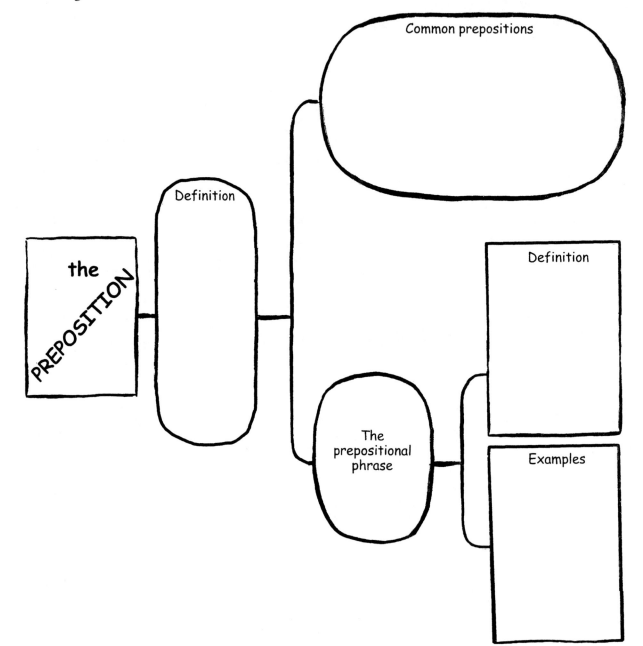

Taking Another Step: On the back of this sheet, write a paragraph about something that interests you, or copy a paragraph from a book. Circle all of the prepositions. Underline all of the prepositional phrases.

　　　　68　　　　*Graphic Organizers for Language Arts Classes*

Name _____ Date _____

G-10: The Conjunction

• **Directions:** The **conjunction** is one of the eight parts of speech. Learn about conjunctions by completing the diagram.

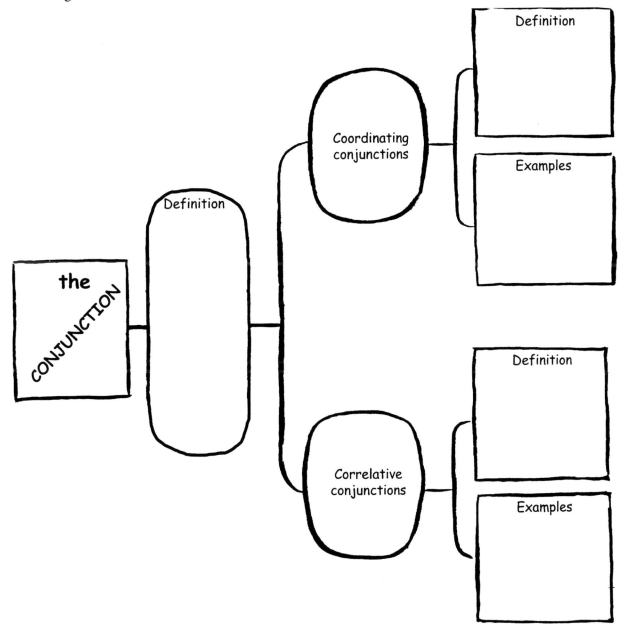

Taking Another Step: On the back of this sheet, write a paragraph about something that interests you, or copy a paragraph from a book. Make a list of all of the conjunctions in the paragraph. Identify what type of conjunction each one is.

Name _____ Date _____

G-11: The Interjection

• **Directions:** The **interjection** is one of the eight parts of speech. Learn about interjections by completing the diagram.

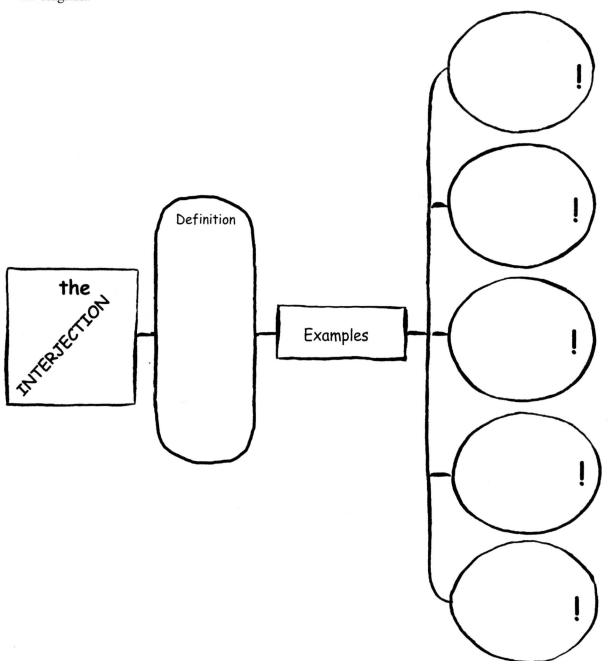

Taking Another Step: On the back of this sheet, write a short dialogue between two made-up characters. Use at least three interjections in the dialogue. Underline them.

                   Graphic Organizers for Language Arts Classes

V. Mechanics: Capitalization and Punctuation

These graphic organizers emphasize learning and memorizing basic rules of capitalization and the proper use of punctuation marks.

M-1: Capitalization

Objective: Students will create a log of important rules for capitalization and give examples of them.

Key Questions:
- What is the rule?
- What are some examples of its use?

Usage Notes: Encourage students to memorize the rules. Encourage students to keep their graphic organizers and update them.

M-2: Punctuation

Objective: Students will identify punctuation marks and explain rules for usage.

Key Questions:
- What is the punctuation mark?
- What are the rules for using this mark?
- What are the mistakes to avoid when using this mark?

Usage Notes: Distribute multiple copies of this graphic organizer (one for each punctuation mark) and have students assemble them into punctuation portfolios.

Name _____ Date _____

M-I: Capitalization

Introduction: One book on language lists no fewer than 67 *rules* for capitalization! Luckily, you'll probably never need to know all of them, and you already know a lot of them. For example, you know that you capitalize names and the first word in a sentence. Knowing these rules and a few others will get you through most situations. Keeping a log of the rules for capitalization is an easy way to remember them.

• **Directions:** As you learn a new rule for capitalization, record it below. Keep this sheet to use as a reference for revising and proofreading your writing assignments.

Some Rules for Capitalization

Rule	Examples

Name _____ Date _____

M-2: Punctuation

• **Directions:** Complete the diagram for a specific punctuation mark.

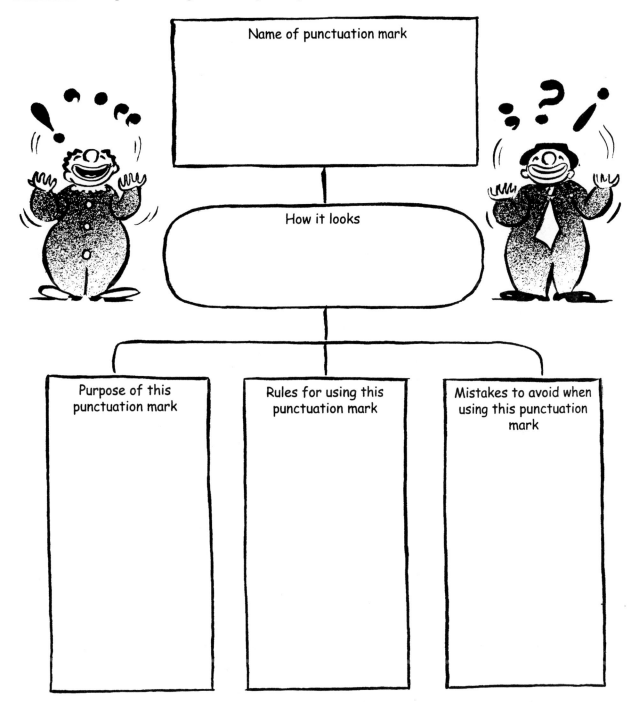

Name of punctuation mark

How it looks

Purpose of this
punctuation mark

Rules for using this
punctuation mark

Mistakes to avoid when
using this punctuation
mark

Taking Another Step: On the back of this sheet, write a few sentences or a paragraph about
something that interests you using the punctuation mark correctly.

75   *Graphic Organizers for Language Arts Classes*

VI.   Additional Graphic Tools

These graphic organizers provide a variety of tools to use in a range of situations, as you see fit. Assign them as appropriate.

Name ______________________________ Date ____________ **Student Activity Sheet**

AGT-1: K-W-L

Introduction: K-W-L stands for What I **K**now, What I **W**ant to Know, and What I **L**earned. Filling out a K-W-L chart before, during, and after a project is a good way for you to keep track of your progress.

• **Directions:** Complete the K-W-L chart.

Activity or Assignment: ______________________________

K (complete before)	W (complete before)	L (complete during and after)
What do you already know about the subject?	What do you want to learn about the subject?	What did you learn about the subject?

Name _____ Date _____

AGT-2: Predictions and Outcomes

• **Directions:** Complete the first two columns of the chart before you read. Complete the last two columns after you read.

Prediction	Reason for My Prediction	Actual Outcome	Lesson I Learned

Name _____ Date _____

AGT-3: The Six Questions

• **Directions:** Write the subject in the center box. Answer each question about the subject in the circles.

Name _____ Date _____

AGT-4: Comparing and Contrasting

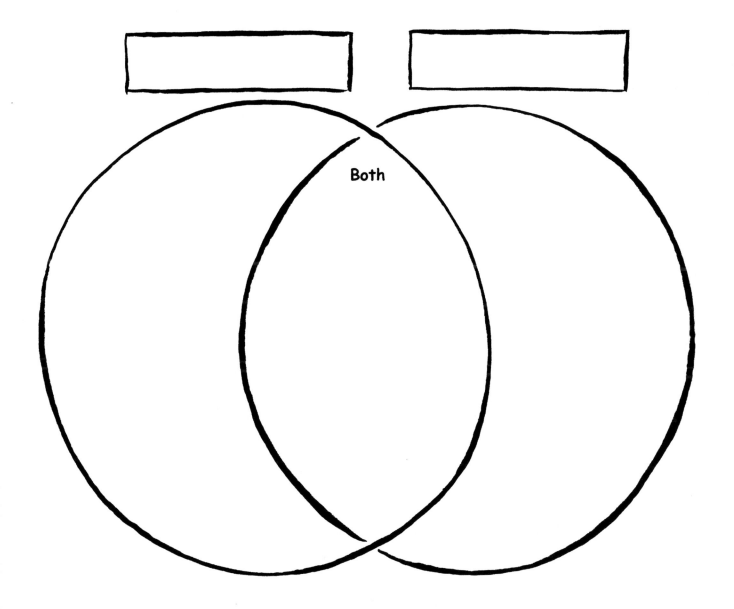

Name _____ Date _____

AGT-5: Main Idea and Details, I

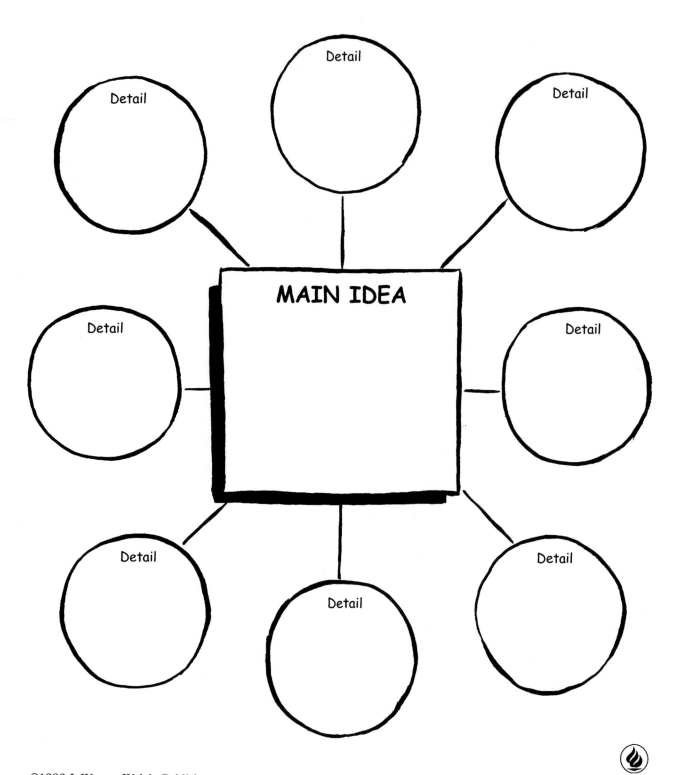

84   *Graphic Organizers for Language Arts Classes*

Name _____ Date _____

AGT-6: Main Ideas and Details, II

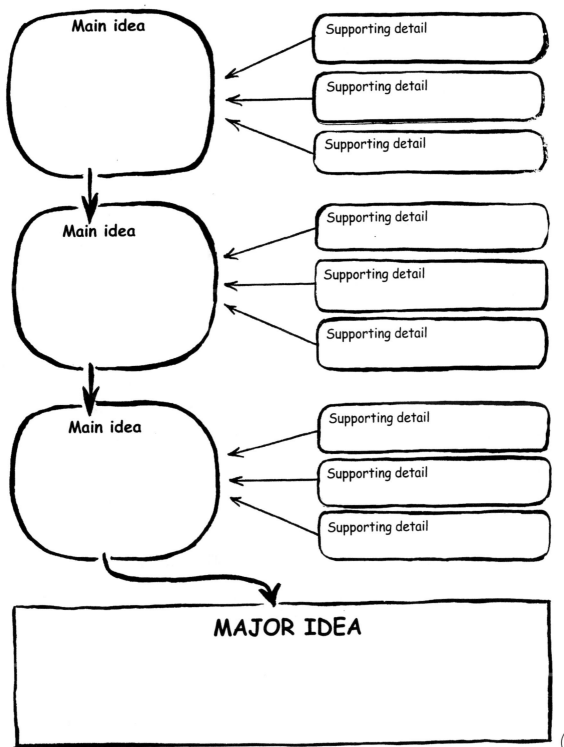

Name _____ Date _____

AGT-7: Main Idea and Details, III

Detail

Detail

Detail

Detail

+

MAIN IDEA

=

Name _____ Date _____

AGT-8: Glossary of Language Arts Terms

Introduction: A **glossary** is a list of specialized terms and their meanings. As you study language arts, you will learn many new terms. This sheet gives you a place to create a personal glossary of these terms.

• **Directions:** As you learn new language arts terms, record them and their meanings in the chart below.

Terms Related to My Study of _____

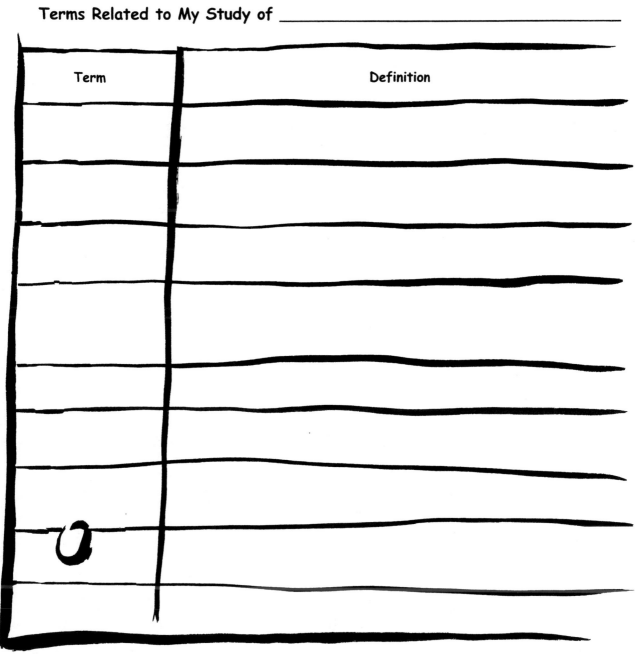

Term	Definition

Share Your Bright Ideas with Us!

We want to hear from you! Your valuable comments and suggestions will help us meet your current and future classroom needs.

Your name_____Date_____

School name_____Phone_____

School address_____

Grade level taught_____Subject area(s) taught_____Average class size_____

Where did you purchase this publication?_____

Was your salesperson knowledgeable about this product?   Yes_____   No_____

What monies were used to purchase this product?

____School supplemental budget   ____Federal/state funding   ____Personal

Please "grade" this Walch publication according to the following criteria:

Quality of service you received when purchasing ....A   B   C   D   F

Ease of use...A   B   C   D   F

Quality of content...A   B   C   D   F

Page layout ....A   B   C   D   F

Organization of material ....A   B   C   D   F

Suitability for grade level ....A   B   C   D   F

Instructional value..A   B   C   D   F

COMMENTS:_____

_____

What specific supplemental materials would help you meet your current—or future—instructional needs?

_____

Have you used other Walch publications? If so, which ones?_____

May we use your comments in upcoming communications?   ____Yes   ____No

Please **FAX** this completed form to **207-772-3105**, or mail it to:

Product Development, J. Weston Walch, Publisher, P.O. Box 658, Portland, ME 04104-0658

We will send you a **FREE GIFT** as our way of thanking you for your feedback. **THANK YOU!**